COUNTING *on* FRANK

For a free color catalog describing Gareth Stevens' list of high-quality children's books, call 1-800-341-3569 (USA) or 1-800-461-9120 (Canada).

Library of Congress Cataloging-in-Publication Data

Clement, Rod.
  Counting on Frank / written and illustrated by Rod Clement.
   p. cm.
  Summary: A boy and his dog present amusing counting, size comparison, and mathematical facts.
  ISBN 0-8368-0358-2
  1. Counting—Juvenile literature. 2. Size perception—Juvenile literature. [1. Mathematics. 2. Size.] I. Title.
QA113.C53 1991
513.5'5—dc20   90-27558

North American edition first published in 1991 by
Gareth Stevens Children's Books
1555 North RiverCenter Drive, Suite 201
Milwaukee, Wisconsin 53212, USA

U.S. edition copyright © 1991. First published in Australia in 1990 by William Collins Pty. Ltd., Sydney, in association with Anne Ingram Books. Text and illustrations © 1990 by Rod Clement.

Printed in the United States of America

1 2 3 4 5 6 7 8 9 95 94 93 92 91

For Sue

COUNTING *on* FRANK

Written and illustrated by
ROD CLEMENT

Gareth Stevens Children's Books
MILWAUKEE

My dad says, "If you've got a brain, then use it!"
So I do.

I sit down and fill my notebook with facts.
Did you know that the average ball-point pen
draws a line twenty-three hundred yards long
before the ink runs out?
My parents consider this fact to be
a bit childish, but I'm sure the
pen company would like to know.

My dog, Frank, is pretty big and takes up
a lot of space.

I calculate that twenty-four Franks could fit
into my bedroom.

But sometimes there isn't even room for one.

If Frank were a humpback whale, however,
only ten would fit into our entire house.
I asked Dad about this, and he said they
would get in the way of the television.

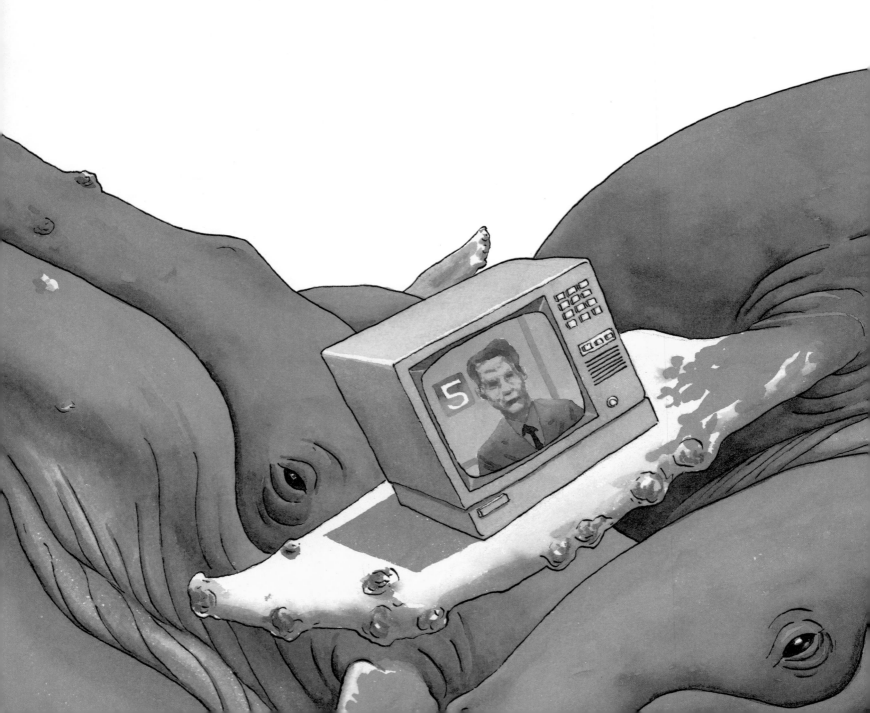

I calculate that only one Dad would
fit inside our big television, but only one-
tenth of him would fit in Mom's portable.

Mom said she would prefer the top part
because Dad's feet smell.

We've got a gum tree in our yard. It grows about six and one-half feet every year.

If I had grown at the same speed, I'd now be fifty-three feet tall! I wouldn't really mind, except I'd never get clothes that fit.

I don't mind taking a bath — it gives me time to think.

For example, I calculate it would take eleven hours and forty-five minutes to fill the entire bathroom with water. That's with both faucets running.

It would take slightly less time to empty, as long as no one opened the door.

When I get dressed, I don't think about fashion or style.
I think about facts.

For instance, it's a fact that if I put on every piece of clothing
in my closet, I would be nine and one-quarter feet tall
and approximately six feet wide.

I would also be unable to
sit down.

I enjoy dinner, not because of the delicious chops Mom cooks EVERY night or the thrilling conversation.

It's the peas.

If I had accidentally knocked fifteen peas off my plate every night for the last eight years, they would now be level with the table top.

Maybe then Mom would understand that her son does *not* like peas.

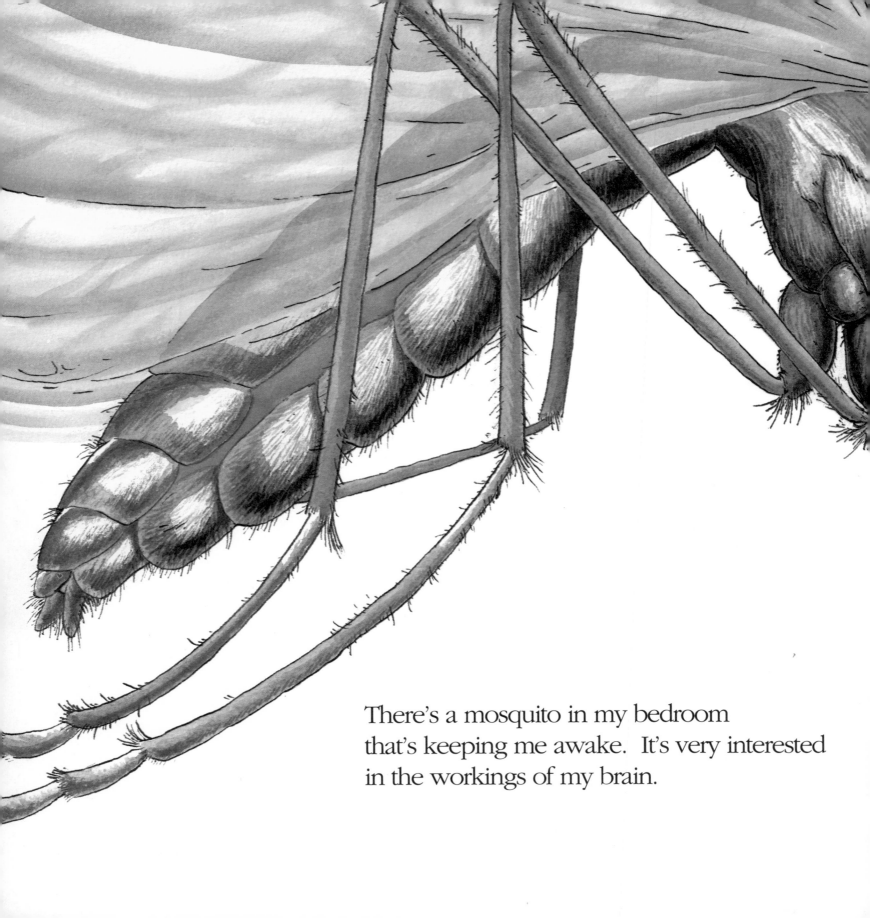

There's a mosquito in my bedroom
that's keeping me awake. It's very interested
in the workings of my brain.

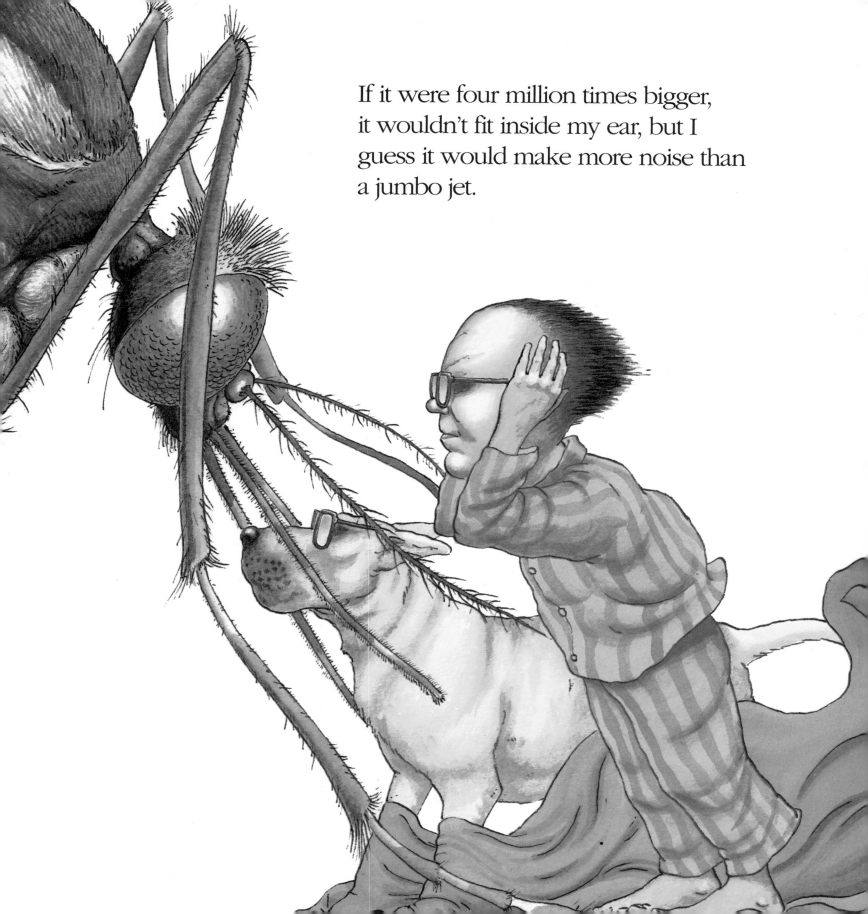

If it were four million times bigger,
it wouldn't fit inside my ear, but I
guess it would make more noise than
a jumbo jet.

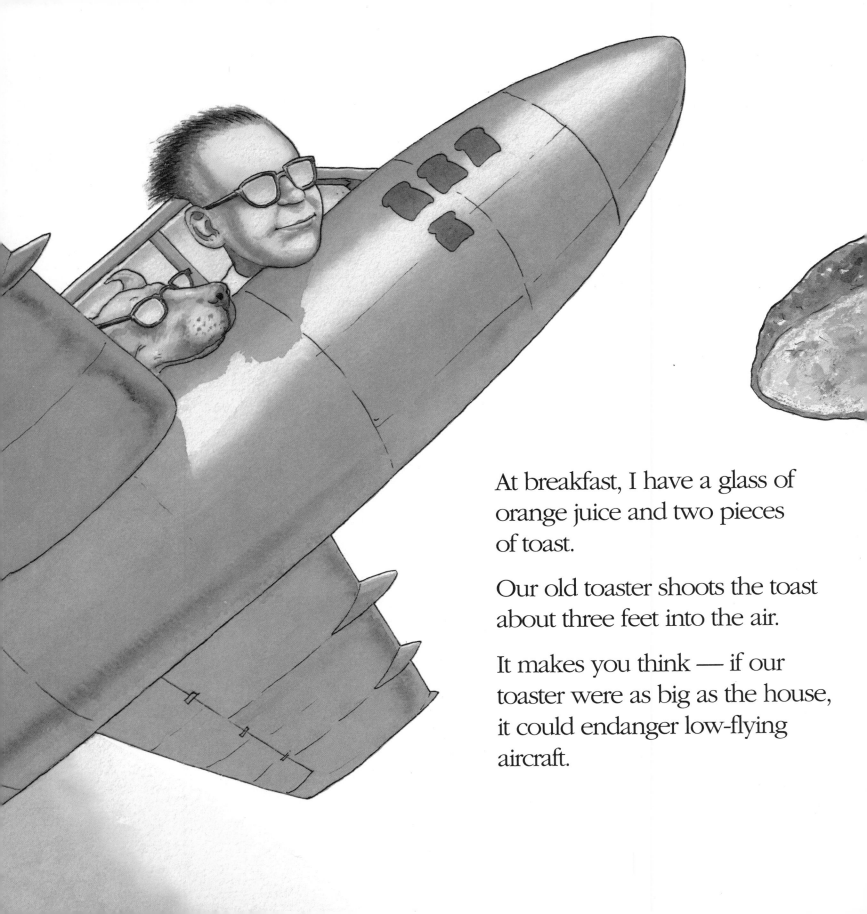

At breakfast, I have a glass of orange juice and two pieces of toast.

Our old toaster shoots the toast about three feet into the air.

It makes you think — if our toaster were as big as the house, it could endanger low-flying aircraft.

Going shopping with Mom is a big event. She is lucky
to have such an intelligent cart pusher.

It takes forty-seven cans of dog food to fill one cart,
but only one to knock over one hundred and ten!

Because of Frank, my knuckles will scrape
along the ground by the time I'm twenty-five!

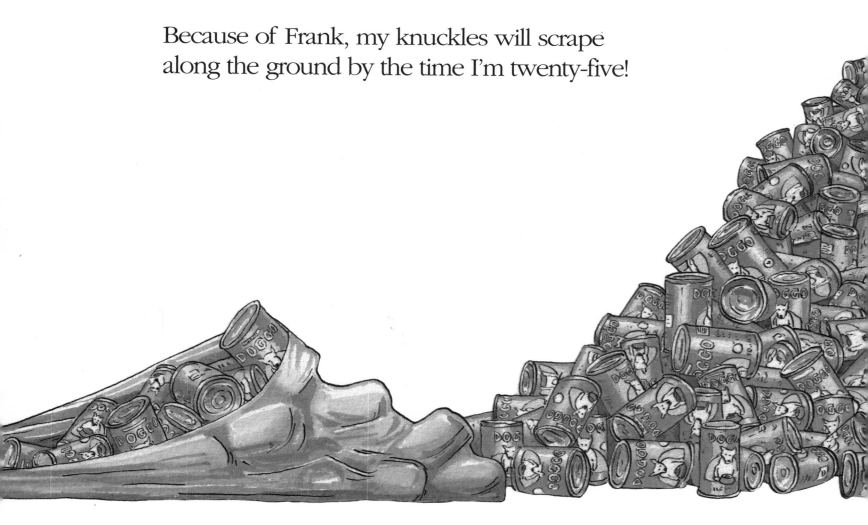

The local club had a competition. You had to
guess how many jellybeans were in a jar, and the
prize was a trip to Hawaii.

They didn't know who they were dealing with.

There are seven hundred and forty-five jellybeans
in the average candy jar. I thought everybody
knew that!

As Dad said on the plane to Hawaii,
"If you've got a brain, then use it."